The Very Best of Paul Cookson

ıul Cookson was born in 1961 and brought up in ıncashire. His early ambitions were to play football for ⸝erton or electric guitar in Slade but he eventually ılified and worked as a full-time teacher for five years. ıce 1989 he has performed his poetry in thousands of nues all over the country. He is widely anthologized and s edited a number of poetry titles. He is also an casional illustrator and his work has been featured on ıtional radio and television. Paul often works with avid Harmer in the popular performance poetry duo ill the Beans. He lives in Retford, Nottinghamshire with s wife, Sally, son Sam and daughter Daisy.

ıvid Parkins has illustrated numerous books, ranging ⸝m maths textbooks to *The Beano*. His picture books ıve been shortlisted for the Smarties Book Prize and the ırt Maschler Award; and commended twice in the Iational Art Library Illustrations Awards. He lives in ᴄincoln with his wife, three children and six cats.

Sch

Also available from Macmillan Children's Books

The Very Best of David Harmer

The Very Best of Wes Magee

The Very Best of Richard Edwards

The Very Best of Vernon Scannell

The Very Best of Ian McMillan

Elephant Dreams
Poems by Ian McMillan, David Harmer
and Paul Cookson

Spill the Beans
Poems by David Harmer and Paul Cookson

The Works
Every Kind of Poem You Will Ever Need
for the Literacy Hour
Chosen by Paul Cookson

Northamptonshire Libraries & Information Service	
Peters	11-Jul-02
821	£3.99

THE VERY BEST OF...

PAUL COOKSON

A Book of Poems

Illustrated by David Parkins

MACMILLAN CHILDREN'S BOOKS

To Daisy and Sam

First published 2001
by Macmillan Children's Books
a division of Pan Macmillan Limited
20 New Wharf Road, London N1 9RR
Basingstoke and Oxford
www.panmacmillan.com

Associated companies throughout the world

ISBN 0 330 48014 6

Text copyright © Paul Cookson 2001
Illustrations copyright © David Parkins 2001

The right of Paul Cookson to be identified as the
author of this book has been asserted by him in accordance
with the Copyright, Designs and Patents Act 1988.

All rights reserved. No part of this publication may be
reproduced, stored in or introduced into a retrieval system, or
transmitted, in any form, or by any means (electronic, mechanical,
photocopying, recording or otherwise) without the prior written
permission of the publisher. Any person who does any unauthorized
act in relation to this publication may be liable to criminal prosecution
and civil claims for damages.

1 3 5 7 9 8 6 4 2

A CIP catalogue record for this book is available from the British Library.

Printed by Mackays of Chatham plc, Chatham, Kent.

This book is sold subject to the condition that it shall not,
by way of trade or otherwise, be lent, re-sold, hired out,
or otherwise circulated without the publisher's prior consent
in any form of binding or cover other than that in
which it is published and without a similar condition including
this condition being imposed on the subsequent purchaser.

Contents

Introduction

Where do you start ? At the beginning I suppose ...

I never knew you could be a poet as a job when I was at school. I remember having to paint a picture in a primary school art class of what I wanted to be when I grew up. I painted a very good picture of a footballer in an Everton shirt, even though I knew then I'd never be good enough. I remember loving writing stories, I even used to write them at home on scraps of Dad's old office paper.

Maybe it started with Slade and Noddy Holder singing 'Cum on feel the noize, girls grab the boyz' – not the most poetical lyric ever, but a favourite nonetheless. One of my favourite couplets of all time comes from Slade's 'Merry Xmas Everybody' – 'Look to the future now, it's only just begun'. Perfect. Simplicity itself and yet it has that ... something. In my early teens I wanted to be in a pop band and wrote several hundred lyrics before moving on to write poetry.

At secondary school Mrs Graham encouraged us to write stories and poems – thanks. By this time I reached sixth form I had read some of D. H. Lawrence's shorter poems. I also discovered Roger McGough and no longer thought of poetry in the same way that I did when reading some secondary school English anthologies. His poems were short, jokey, sometimes just a couple of lines based around a pun. I'd also seen John Cooper Clarke perform at Preston Guildhall and he was like no other poet I'd ever seen. Things were starting to change. I could name other poets whose work influenced me but the list would be endless – Brian Patten, Steve Turner, Stewart Henderson ... I remember a little paperback collection called *Rhinoceros* by a poet called Simon Jenkins that he sold for a pound.

As a result of that little book, in 1979, at the age of 18 I saved up and produced my first collection of poems – *Growing Older Soon* – which I sold for 50p each. I was to do several more of these in the next few years. Poetry was more than a hobby but not yet a job. My job was teaching and my poetry was not really for children, although I had used my own childhood as a basis for a collection called *Batman and Oddy* (which had been in turn inspired by Mike Harding's *The Singing Street*).

I met a poet called Henry Normal who really encouraged my performance work. He then introduced me to Ian McMillan and Martyn Wiley. Sitting in Sheffield railway station chatting after appearing on their Saturday morning radio show I asked whether poetry could be my job as well as my hobby. 'Write poems for children, visit schools' said Ian. Advice I took to heart. Within a year of that conversation I had become a part-time teacher, written lots of new poems and started to visit schools. My writing changed. My job changed. For the better.

If it hadn't been for Ian I wouldn't have met my good friend and poetical partner in rhyme, David Harmer. We've been performing as Spill The Beans for ten years or so, mainly to people who don't think that they're going to like poetry then buy a book at the end of the show.

People often get snobby about poetry, especially poetry for children but I think it's a fantastically exciting area to be working in. I love the uproarious laughter it can cause and I love the silence when a poem touches a nerve. As I've got older I've realized that poetry can be everything – funny, sad, thoughtful, weird, rude, depressing, thought-provoking, angry or just plain daft – and that it can be written in lots of different styles. There isn't a wrong or right way. Anyone can do it – that's why I love going round schools and doing workshops where everyone can succeed. Everyone has ideas so everyone can write poetry. Simple as that. Poetry isn't just for a chosen, educated few in language that not everyone understands, poetry is for (and by) everyone.

I don't really have a definition of poetry, although one that I like is 'it's that stuff that has the white space round the edges and lines don't go to the end of the page' or as Ian McMillan says, 'Performance poetry is like ordinary language turned up a bit'.

I hope you enjoy these as much as I enjoyed not only writing them, but performing them and revisiting some of them. Whatever, I hope that at least a few of them have that certain . . . something for you.

Poetry's been my job for over ten years now. It's never boring. Writing, performing, choosing poems, putting books together. I can't think of a better job. It's been a funny old journey since painting that picture, but the journey's not over yet, not by a long chalk. As Noddy sings, 'Look to the future, it's only just begun'.

Have fun!

Paul Cookson

I Would Win the Gold
if These Were Olympic Sports . . .

Bubble gum blowing
Goggle box watching
Late morning snoring
Homework botching

Quilt ruffling
Little brother teasing
Pizza demolishing
Big toe cheesing

Insult hurling, wobbly throwing
Infinite blue belly button fluff growing

Late night endurance computer screen gazing
Non-attentive open-jawed eyeball glazing

Ultimate volume decibel blaring
Long-distance marathon same sock wearing

Recognize all these as sports then meet . . .
Me! The Champ Apathetic Athlete!

Father's Hands

Father's hands
large like frying pans
broad as shovel blades
strong as weathered spades.

Father's hands
finger ends ingrained with dirt
permanently stained from work
ignoring pain and scorning hurt.

I once saw him walk boldly up to a swan
that had landed in next door's drive and wouldn't move.
The police were there because swans are a protected
    species,
but didn't do anything, but my dad walked up to it,
picked it up and carried it away. No problem.
Those massive wings that can break a man's bones
were held tight, tight by my father's hands
and I was proud of him that day, really proud.

Father's hands
tough as leather on old boots
firmly grasping nettle shoots
pulling thistles by their roots.

Father's hands
gripping like an iron vice
never numb in snow and ice
nails and screws are pulled and prised.

He once found a kestrel with a broken wing
and kept it in our garage until it was better.
He'd feed it by hand with scraps of meat or dead mice
and you could see where its beak and talons
had taken bits of skin from his finger ends.
It never seemed to hurt him at all, he just smiled
as he let it claw and peck.

Father's hands
lifting bales of hay and straw
calloused, hardened, rough and raw
building, planting, painting . . . more.

Father's hands
hard when tanning my backside
all we needed they supplied
and still my hands will fit inside

Father's hands
large like frying pans
broad as shovel blades
strong as weathered spades.

And still my hands will fit inside
my father's hands.

Superman's Dog

Superman's dog – he's the best
Helping pets in distress
Red and gold pants and vest
'SD' on his chest.

Superman's dog – X-ray sight
Green bones filled with Kryptonite
Bright blue Lycra tights in flight
Faster than a meteorite

Better than Batman's robin
Rougher than Robin's bat
Faster than Spiderman's spider
Cooler than Catwoman's cat

Superman's dog – bionic scent
Crime prevention – his intent
Woof and tough – cement he'll dent
What's his name – Bark Kent!

The Day After the Day After Boxing Day

On the day after the day after Boxing Day
Santa wakes up, eventually,
puts away his big red suit and wellies,
lets Rudolph and the gang out into the meadow
then shaves his head and beard.

He puts on his new cool sunglasses,
baggy blue Bermuda shorts (he's sick of red),
yellow stripy T-shirt that doesn't quite cover his belly
and lets his toes breathe in flip-flops.

Packing a bucket and spade,
fifteen tubes of Factor Twenty suncream
and seventeen romantic novels
he fills his Walkman with the latest sounds,
is glad to use a proper suitcase instead of the old sack
and heads off into the Mediterranean sunrise
enjoying the comforts of a Boeing 747
(although he passes on the free drinks).

Six months later,
relaxed, red and a little more than stubbly,
he looks at his watch, adjusts his wide-brimmed sunhat,
mops the sweat from his brow and strokes his chin,
wondering why holidays always seem to go so quickly.

Man's Best Friend

He's not a bad pet really . . .
I've had him years now
I've got used to his ways
I suppose he's got used to mine as well.

He's not as young as he used to be . . .
His eyesight's going
And sometimes he can be a bit deaf.
When he wants to be!

He's put on some extra weight too . . .
I take him for walks
But they're getting shorter and less frequent these days.
He's not as energetic as he once was.

We don't really play any games now . . .
He can't catch the frisbee any more,
Sticks are left alone and when the football burst
There didn't seem much point in buying another.

He sleeps most of the time . . .
Seems to like it by the fire best these days
With a warm tartan rug
And the comforting sound of the television.

Occasionally he perks up a bit . . .
Especially if it involves chocolate,
Homemade ginger cake from Mrs Bingham next door
Or a visit from the grandchildren.

But mostly it's like this . . .
Peaceful
Comfortable
Friendly.

We look after each other these days . . .
I trust him with my life.
Best friends, I wouldn't swap him for anything.
We've seen some things!

Yes, he's the best master any dog could wish for.

Where Teachers Keep Their Pets

Mrs Cox has a fox
nesting in her curly locks.

Mr Spratt's tabby cat
sleeps beneath his bobble hat.

Miss Cahoots has various newts
swimming in her zip-up boots.

Mr Spry has Fred his fly
eating food stains from his tie.

Mrs Groat shows off her stoat
round the collar of her coat.

Mr Spare's got grizzly bears
hiding in his spacious flares.

And . . .

Mrs Vickers has a stick insect called
'Stickers'
and she keeps it in her . . .

Four Crazy Pets

I've four crazy pets, all rather jolly –
Rover, Tiddles, Flopsy and Polly.
A dog, a rabbit, a parrot and a cat.
Which one's which? Can you guess that?

Rover's a dog? No!
Tiddles is a cat? No!
Flopsy's a rabbit? No!
Polly's a parrot? No!

My dog has the appetite of a small gorilla.
We called her Polly 'cause we can never fill her.

The rabbit has a habit of wetting where we're standing.
We call him Tiddles 'cause the puddles keep expanding.

Our cat purrs like an engine turning over
Vroom vroom vroom – so we call her Rover.

The fact that our parrot cannot fly is such a shame.
Flopsy by nature and Flopsy by name.

Four crazy names! Wouldn't you agree?
I think my pets fit their names perfectly.

Prrrrr!
Prrrrr!

Flip!
Flop!
Flap!

November 6th – Last Night's Life

Last night's magic, last night's colours,
Last night's sparkle, last night's fizz,
Last night's snap, last night's crackle,
Last night's pop, last night's whizz.

Last night's boom, last night's crash,
Last night's bangs today are found
Blackened, ash-stained, shattered cardboard,
Dead and scattered on the ground.

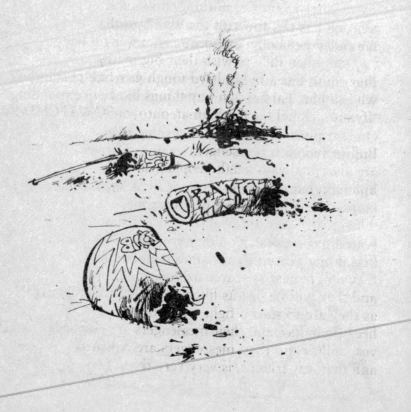

Bullies and Their Messengers

Have you noticed how bullies always have gangs
and never ever walk alone?
They never speak to you one to one,
it's always some little messenger
who comes up to you and says,
'WatchityordedcosmybigmatesgonnagetyouRIGHT!'

Bullies' messengers are always small.
Always.
By themselves they're nothing, nobodies,
who hide in shadows on the way home,
never saying boo to a goose
. . . but when they're with their big mates
they think they are big hard tough guy fighters
who say big hard tough guy things like,
'IfyoutouchmeI'llgetmybigmateontoyouSOWATCHIT!'

Bullies and their messengers
are always always small people inside,
hiding in large groups,
pretending that they're really tough
when really they are frightened nobodies
scared to be alone,
and if by chance you do catch them alone
they will be just as scared as you might be
and they will be just as likely to walk away silently
as they are to start a fight with you
because bullies and their messengers are cowards
yes, bullies and their messengers are cowards
and that, my friends, is very very true.

Barry and Beryl
the Bubble Gum Blowers

Barry and Beryl the bubble gum blowers
blew bubble gum bubbles as big as balloons.
All shapes and sizes, zebras and zeppelins,
swordfish and sea lions, sharks and baboons,
babies and buckets, bottles and biplanes,
buffaloes, bees, trombones and bassoons
Barry and Beryl the bubble gum blowers
blew bubble gum bubbles as big as balloons.

Barry and Beryl the bubble gum blowers
blew bubble gum bubbles all over the place.
Big ones in bed, on back seats of buses,
blowing their bubbles in baths with bad taste,
they blew and they bubbled from breakfast till bedtime
the biggest gum bubble that history traced.
One last big breath . . . and the bubble exploded
bursting and blasting their heads into space.
Yes, Barry and Beryl the bubble gum blowers
blew bubbles that blasted their heads into space.

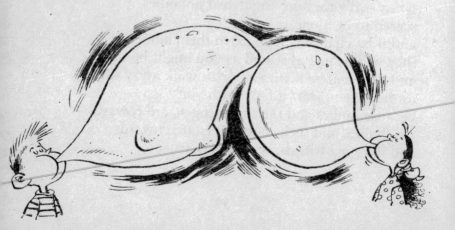

Billy Doesn't Like School Really

Billy doesn't like school really.
It's not because he can't do the work
but because some of the other kids
don't seem to like him that much.

They call him names
and make up jokes about his mum.
Everyone laughs . . . except Billy.
Everyone laughs . . . except Billy.

They all think it's OK
because it's only a laugh and a joke
and they don't really mean it anyway
but Billy doesn't know that.

Billy doesn't know that
and because of that
Billy doesn't like school really.

Short Visit, Long Stay

The school trip was a special occasion
But we never reached our destination
Instead of the Zoo
I was locked in the loo
Of an M62 Service Station.

Autumn Leaves

Autumn leaves leave
leaving Autumn trees
leafless.

Let No One Steal Your Dreams

Let no one steal your dreams
Let no one tear apart
The burning of ambition
That fires the drive inside your heart.

Let no one steal your dreams
Let no one tell you that you can't
Let no one hold you back
Let no one tell you that you won't.

Set your sights and keep them fixed
Set your sights on high
Let no one steal your dreams
Your only limit is the sky.

Let no one steal your dreams
Follow your heart
Follow your soul
For only when you follow them
Will you feel truly whole.

Set your sights and keep them fixed
Set your sights on high
Let no one steal your dreams
Your only limit is the sky.

Epitaph for the Last Martian

Crash landing caused extinction
The last of the Martian species
Here and here and here and here
He rests in pieces.

Wuthering Frights

Our English teacher's wild and
untamed classic stood before us.
Her very literary pet,
Miss Emily's Brontë Saurus.

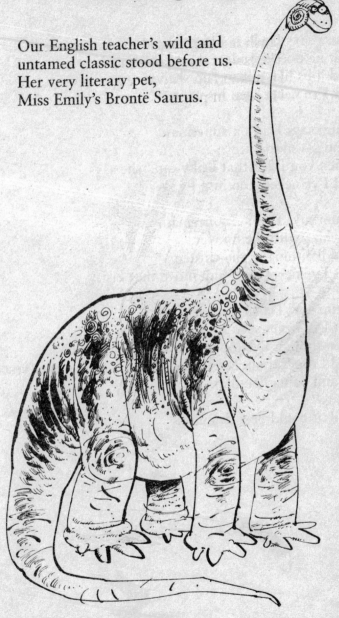

Mum Says Dad's a Superman

Mum says Dad's a superman,
that he does wonders round the house,
odd jobs like putting up shelves
but I've never seen his cape.

Mum says Dad's a superman,
'You saved my life
when you fixed that leaky tap,' she says
but I've never seen him fly.

Mum says Dad's a superman,
a whizz with the hoover
and lightning in the garden
but I've never seen him move that fast.

Mum says Dad's a superman,
but I've never seen his big red pants
even though I've looked on the washing line
and I don't think Superman would wear a string vest
    and pants like that.

Still, it could be a disguise.

Mother is a Skinhead

Mother is a skinhead
Brother's heavy metal
Sister's into flower power
So we call her Petal.

Her boyfriend Shane likes techno
He's always on the rave
Grandma is a rapper Yo!
She repeats everything she says
She repeats everything she says.

Dad dresses like Elvis
And greases back his hair.
Grandad likes the seventies
With platform boots and flares.

Uncle Frank's from Worksop
Old punk and tattered clothes
Chains and rings and padlocks
Join his ears to his nose.

Great-Gran dances go-go
She likes to shake her thing.
The parrot's into jungle
The budgie's into swing.

Heavy rock at ninety-four years old
Affected Uncle Fred
His bathchair now does ninety-five
And he's got tattoos on his bald head.

Great-Aunt Clara's purple rinse
Shines out like a beacon
Now it's been replaced
With a pink and green Mohican.

Auntie Rene, once removed,
From Italy likes opera.
Uncle Clive likes to jive
But always lands on top of her.

Cousin Ray likes reggae
The baby sings the blues
The dog and cat like rock and roll
Both wear blue suede shoes.

Me . . . I don't like music
Can't sing or play guitar
So I've got the perfect qualities
To be a top pop star.

Rock around the clock, morning, noon and night
No one ever argues, no one ever fights
In tune with each other, a happy family
We'd like to teach the world to sing and live in
      harmony.

This Year I Will Stay Awake

This year I will stay awake
all night long, make no mistake.
On this Christmas Eve I'll keep
my eyes open, try to peep.
This year I won't drowse or dream
but be alert till Santa's been,
see just what he leaves and how
he fits down our chimney now,
how the presents all appear,
hear the sleigh bells and reindeer.
This year I will not count sheep
but pretend to be asleep.
No catnaps or snoozing but I
won't drop off and get some shut-eye.

This year there will be no slumber
I won't let myself go under.
No forty winks or throwing zeds.
No blinking, kipping, heavy headszz . . .
This year I won't nod or doze
or let my heavy eyelids close.
This year I won't nod or doze
or let my heavy eyelids close
or let my heavy eyelids close
or let my he . . . avy eye . . . li . . . ds clo . . . se
or let my he . . . avy eye . . . liiids cl . . . oozzzzzzzzzzzzzzzz

A Christmas Not Present

December 16th, 6.40 a.m.
I'm on a train going south
travelling further away from home.

Later on today my son makes his debut,
a speaking part in the infant nativity,
two lines, very well rehearsed.

I've heard these lines over and over . . . and over again,
often in different orders,
but now, word perfect.

Of course I know the story.
Of course I'm familiar with the plot . . .
but it's not quite the same.

The camcorder will capture the moment
for me to see later, again and again . . . and over again
but it's not quite the same.

I'd rather pause . . .
rewind
be there and feel the magic of the moment.

Just for Another Minute

On the eleventh of the eleventh
at eleven o'clock
we all stopped.

We all stopped doing maths,
put our pens down
and closed our eyes for a minute.

A whole minute.

At first I wanted to work out the answer
to the question I was stuck on,
then I wanted to think about football . . .
but I couldn't, I just couldn't.

The silence made me think about poppies
and the old men in medals who sold them
down the shopping centre.

The old men with walking sticks who once carried guns
and fought in a war I could not understand.
A real war, not like on the videos.

And even though I didn't know anyone like that
I was sad, just a little bit sad.

Before I knew it the minute was over
and the silence was gone
but I wanted it to carry on,
I wanted to carry on thinking,
I wanted the silence again.

Just for another minute.

The Longest Day of the Year

It is the longest day of the year.
Extra daylight hours
That I could use for inspiration
To write a poem celebrating
The longest day of the year.

It is the longest day of the year
And here I am, stuck inside,
Writing a poem about it being
The longest day of the year
When really I want to go out.

The sun is shining,
There's not a cloud in the sky,
The birds are singing
And the longest day of the year
Should be a good day for poems.

But it isn't.
It's a good day to take off your socks,
Paddle in the sea,
Make sandcastles,
Eat the largest ice cream you can find
And maybe, just maybe,
Maybe write a poem in the sand
For the waves to wash away.

The Shortest Day of the Year

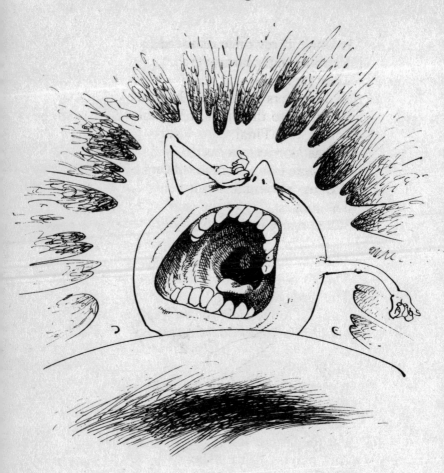

Lazy sun
Clocks in late
Clocks off early
If at all.

My Uncle Percy Once Removed

My Uncle Percy once removed
his bobble hat, scarf, overcoat,
woolly jumper, string vest,
flared trousers and purple Y-fronts
and ran on to the pitch at Wembley
during a Cup Final
and was at once removed
by six stewards and nine officers of the law.
Once they'd caught him.

Poetry So Ordinary You Do Not Need a Dictionary

Some people say that real poetry
is the poetry that stands the test of time
immortalized in print
in the language of the gods
in leather-bound volumes
on yellowing pages
and discussed at length by intellectuals.

Me?

I want to write poetry that captures the here and now
and celebrates that fleeting moment.

Poetry that puts its finger on
exactly what you're feeling this very minute.

Poetry that hits the nail on the head
and then moves on or is forgotten.

Poetry that tells you jokes and trivia
and makes you laugh, cry or just remember.

Poetry that weaves its way into your mind
for the same length of time you hum the latest number
    one hit.

Poetry that makes you say,
'Yeah . . . I've thought that as well.'

Poetry that uses words like snot, snog and bum
and has no snobbery or embarrassment.

Poetry for everyone, young or old
and especially those not interested in poetry.

Poetry that masquerades as nothing else
than words on a page that you may or may not like.

Poetry so ordinary
that you can understand it without the use of a
    dictionary.

Poetry that makes you want to remember it
and tell it to a friend.

Poetry that makes you think
that you could write it too . . . and probably write it
    better.

And if I do just one of these
then maybe, just maybe, the poetry I write
will have been worthwhile.

Till Playtime Do Us Part and the Lovehearts are all Eaten

One kiss and that was it.
Love.
I say one kiss but it wasn't even a proper one.
He went to kiss her on the cheek,
she turned around dead embarrassed
so all he got was a mouthful of hair . . . and a nosebleed.
But it was still love.

One kiss behind the school wall at playtime
and that was it.
Love. True love.
They decided to get married.

They'd bring each other presents.
He'd bring her his favourite Football Team swap cards,
his seventy-fiver conker and his best set of tadpoles.
She'd give him her favourite lucky charm
(a plastic My Little Pony on a key ring),
and sweets covered in fluff from the bottom of her
    schoolbag.

So he gave up playing football at playtimes
and she tied big knots in her skipping rope.

They'd sit for hours and hours and hours
gazing deeply into each other's eyes
until they went cross-eyed and dizzy,
eating packets and packets and packets of Lovehearts
reading the messages out to each other in dead soppy
    voices:

'Be mine forever'
'Hiya cutie'
'Love ya lots 'n' lots'
'You snog dead good'

Nine and a half years old and they got married,
curtain rings and stolen flowers,
muddy-kneed and laughing,
the whole class drank Dandelion and Burdock.

Their friends told them it wouldn't last.
They were right.
Two weeks later she left him.
She went off with a brand-new bike
and fell in love with a pop star from Manchester
(designer clothes, no spots and toothpaste smile).
So he went off with the school football team
and dreamed of scoring the winning goal at Wembley.

Mum for a Day

Mum's ill in bed today
so I said I'd do the housework
and look after things.
She told me it was really hard
but I said it would be dead easy
so . . .

I hoovered the sink
dusted the cat
cooked Dad's shoes and socks
washed up the carpet in the dishwasher
fed the ornaments
polished the steak and kidney pudding
ironed the letters and parcels
posted the shirts and knickers
and hung the budgie out to dry.

It took me all day but I got everything finished
and I was really tired
and I'm really glad Mum isn't ill
    every day.
So is the budgie.

The Toilet Seat Has Teeth

The bathroom has gone crazy
far beyond belief.
The sink is full of spiders
and the toilet seat has teeth!

The plughole in the bath
has a whirlpool underneath
that pulls you down feet first
and the toilet seat has teeth!

The toothpaste tube is purple
and makes your teeth fall out.
The toilet roll is nettles
and makes you scream and shout!

The towels have got bristles,
the bubble bath is glue,
the soap has turned to jelly
and it makes your skin bright blue.

The mirror's pulling faces
at everyone it can
The shower's dripping marmalade
and blackcurrant jam.

The rubber ducks are breeding
and building their own nest
with shaving foam and tissues
in Grandad's stringy vest.

Shampoo is liquid dynamite,
there's petrol in the hairspray,
both will cure dandruff
when they blow your head away!

The bathroom has gone crazy
far beyond belief.
The sink is full of spiders
and the toilet seat has teeth!

The plughole in the bath
has a whirlpool underneath
that pulls you down feet first
and the toilet seat has teeth!

The toilet seat has teeth! Ow!
The toilet seat has teeth! Ow!
The toilet seat has teeth! Ow!
The toilet seat has teeth! Ow!

Crunch! Slurp! Munch! Burp!
The toilet seat has teeth! Ow!
Don't – sit – on – it!
The toilet seat has . . .! Owwwww!

Mum Used Prittstick

Mum used Prittstick
Instead of lipstick
Then went and kissed my dad.

Two days passed
Both stuck fast.
The longest snog they ever had.

Figuratively Speaking

If I speak in pictures
Then your ears must be my canvas
And my tongue a brush that paints the words
I want you to imagine.

The Magician's Composition of a Spell of Great Precision

The magician with ambition was a mystical physician
who sought the composition of a spell of great
precision.
For all things scientific
his knowledge was prolific:
voltage and transmission, gaseous ignition,
simple recognition of nuclear collision
and specific hieroglyphics was wicked and terrific.

The wizard of decision was a great mathematician,
a master statistician of addition and division.
For all things mathematical
his brain was acrobatical:
fractions and subtractions, factors and reactions,
equation complications, long multiplications,
computations problematical his mind was telepathical.

The solution's constitution was brought unto fruition,
magic spells and sorcery defying definition.
An amazing combination of enchanting calculations.
A wonderful creation beyond imagination.
A crazy composition of wish and superstition
fulfilling the ambition of this magician's vision
the lotions and the potions made him such a rich 'un
thanks to their transmission on national television.

Big Plans for a Big Empire

Bodjitea, the Chief Builder,
stuck his pencil behind his ear,
whistled through his teeth
then tut tut tutted
as he stood in front of the Emperor and Master
Architect.

'It'll cost you, this lot,' he said
while shaking his head at the plans.
'It's not cheap, *and* it'll be a long job,
all these fancy buildings and temples and things,
not to mention those straight roads and the drains.
Plus the baths are a bit ornate too.
Take some time they will.
'Course, I'll need labour costs,
time and a half for the lads at weekends
and double time on any holy days or feast days.'

'You want it finished when?
You'll be lucky!
Rome wasn't built in a day, you know.'

My Dad the Headmaster

My dad the headmaster knows every single rule
and when he is at home he thinks that he's at school.
He rings the bell each morning and I'd better not be late
so I'm washed and down for breakfast at exactly ten to
    eight.

He stands and takes the register, checks my shirt and tie,
then says, 'Good Morning' and I have to reply
'Good Morn – ing, Fa – ther' in the monotone drone
and hear his assembly in my very own home.

He has a list of rules that are pasted on each door:
No Spitting. No Chewing. No Litter On The Floor.
No Music. No Jewellery. No Make-up. No Telly.
No Making Rude Noises Especially If They're Smelly.

No Videos. No Football. No Coloured Socks Or Laces.
No Trainers. No Jeans. No Smiling Faces.
No Sticking Bubble Gum In Your Sister's Hair.
No Wiping Bogeys Down The Side Of The Chair.

He has a list of sayings for all types of occasion
and set of phrases for every situation:
'Don't run down the stairs. Speak when spoken to.
Put your hand up first if you want to use the loo.'

'I don't mind how long I wait. Listen when I'm
    speaking.
No one leaves the table until we've all all finished eating.
Don't interrupt and don't answer back.
Don't do this and don't do that.'

Yes, my dad the headmaster knows every single rule
and when he is at home he thinks that he's at school.
But I'm not the only one who does what he is told.
Dad never complains if his dinner is cold.

He's ever so polite when Mother is around
and mumbles, 'Yes, my dear' while looking at the
     ground.
Her foghorn commands, they really drive him crazy.
Dad's scared of Mum 'cause she's a dinner lady!

Poem for the First Day of the Football Season

Brand-new start,
last season is history and meaningless.

My team has no points
and neither has yours.

All things are possible
and all glory dreamable.

Everything is winnable.
Potential is unmissable.

The peak of faith is scaleable.
The mountain of hope is touchable.
The summit of belief, believable.

Ten to three on that first Saturday
and nothing dulls the taste.

Excitement and anticipation
tangible and tasteable.

Unparalleled success attainable.
This could be the best season of our lives.

The Last Day of the Football Season

Dreams in tatters
Hopes in rags
Blown away
Like paper bags

Early exits
From each cup
My team down
Your team up

Shadows lengthen
The worst I fear
But I'll be back
Same time next year.

Teacher

Loud shouter
Deep thinker
Rain hater
Coffee drinker

Spell checker
Sum ticker
Line giver
Nit picker

Ready listener
Trouble carer
Hometime lover
Knowledge sharer.

Jack Frost

Jack Frost,
Winter wizard
Brightens up the darkest night
Spells while we are fast asleep.

Jack Frost,
Winter jeweller
Encrusting spiders' webs with diamonds,
Icicle fingertips, silver breath.

Jack Frost,
Winter graffiti artist
Spray can magic, leaves his mark,
Christmas card scenery, the icing on the lake.

...ing Captain Concorde

BLAST OFF!

Is it a ...
Is it a plane?
Look at the size of the nose on his face!
Is it a bird?
Is it a plane?
Captain Concorde is his name!
Captain Concorde NEEOWN!
What a big nose NEEOWN!

He's a man with a mission
Radar vision
A nose that's supersonic
Faster than the speed of sound
His Y-fronts are bionic
Big and baggy
Red and saggy
Streamlined underpants
Always ready
High-tech shreddies
Crooks don't stand a chance . . .

Is it a bird?
Is it a plane?
Look at the size of the nose on his face!
Is it a bird?
Is it a plane?
Captain Concorde is his name!
Captain Concorde NEEOWN!
What a big nose NEEOWN!

Anytime anyplace anywhere
But never ever Mondays
Cos that's the day the Captain's mum
Washes his red undies.
Anytime anyplace anywhere
His power is fantastic
Everything's under control
With super-strength elastic!
Anytime anywhere anyplace
But bathrooms are a no no
Cos the toilet seat has teeth! OW!
And then it's time to go so . . .

Is it a bird?
Is it a plane?
Look at the size of the nose on his face!
Is it a bird?
Is it a plane?
Captain Concorde is his name!
Captain Concorde NEEOWN!
What a big nose NEEOWN!

The Amazing Captain Concorde . . . he's a superman.
The Amazing Captain Concorde . . . super underpants.
The Amazing Captain Concorde . . . nobody can trick
    him
The Amazing Captain Concorde . . . with a nose like
    that you'd pick him

Who's the man with the supersonic nose? . . . Captain
    Concorde!
Who's the man with the terrible taste in clothes? . . .
    Captain Concorde!
Who's the man who's always your best friend? . . .
    Captain Concorde!
Who's the man who always sets the trends? . . . Captain
    Concorde!

Who's the man who's so aerodynamic? . . . Captain
    Concorde!
Who's the man who makes all villains panic? . . .
    Captain Concorde!
Who's the man who always helps his mum? . . . Captain
    Concorde!
Who's the man you'd like to become? . . . Captain
    Concorde!
Who? Captain Concorde!
Who? Captain Concorde!
Soooooo . . .

Is it a bird?
Is it a plane?
Look at the size of the nose on his face!
Is it a bird?
Is it a plane?
Captain Concorde is his name!
Captain Concorde NEEOWN!
What a big nose NEEOWN!

A DIY Poem about a Peticular Disaster

In this poem we have the following:

1.   My brother
2.   My brother's pet stick insects
        (which he keeps in a glass bowl)
3.   My grandad
4.   My mum

The following things happen, in any order:

1.   Mum puts a bowl of Twiglets on the table
2.   Grandad takes his glasses off
3.   Grandad eats some Twiglets
4.   My brother cleans out his stick insects

There is, however, a terrible mix-up.
Can you guess what it is?

Arthur, My Half-Cousin

One eye, one ear, one nostril
One arm, one leg, one hand
Arthur, my half-cousin
Is half the boy I am.

One knee, one foot, one ankle
I'm twelve, he's half a dozen
I'm twice the boy that Arthur is
Arthur – half a cousin.

It Wasn't Me

It wasn't me, sir, honest, sir.
It wasn't me, sir, it was him.
I wasn't with him, honest, sir.
It was definitely him, sir
but I definitely wasn't with him, honest, sir.
Honest, sir, I'm telling the truth,
it wasn't me, it was him, sir.
It can't have been me, sir,
I wasn't with him.
Honest, sir.

I was quite near him though.

Scarborough Summer Snapshots

Seagull vultures cry
a massed chorus of shrieking
echoing echoing echoing
like a needle stuck in a groove.

      Clouds scurry by
      on the vast blue underbelly of the sky,
      surfers on their own white waves.

Whispering grass, crackling paper
and the hollow empty laughter of Coca Cola cans,
the only conversations on the wind-blown sea wall.

      Incoming tide
      blue with crescents white
      spreading a cloak of beautiful deceit:
      water in the open mouth
      of sharp-fanged teeth.

Racing on the crest of a breeze
clouds sprint like lemmings to the edge of the cliff
then fade and d
         i
          e.

      Bodiless shirts billow,
      frantic and excited.
      Limbless trousers run the races
      of ten thousand marathons
      yet never tire,
      fuelled by an invisible relentless force.

Distant echoes
laughter, shouting, ice cream bells
and seagull cries
fade in then out of earshot
like flies alighting on a page
or the bright warm focus of the sun
changing into shade.

The bright blue curtain of the sky
slowly closes from my view
as folding clouds billow
and slowly join together.

Rippling teeth of waves
comb the tussled beach.

Picnic leftovers
picked and looked over,
pecked and lent over
by small brown sparrows.

Summer bright
Summer hot
Summer sunny
Summer not.

'L' Plates on My Football Shirt

When I play football for the football team at school
no one takes me seriously, they think I'm just a fool.
My right boot's on my left foot, my left is on my right,
my socks are on my arms and my shorts are far too
    tight.

I have shin pads on my chin just in case I'm fouled.
My shirt is full of holes, inside out and upside down.
The laces on my boots are nearly five miles long.
I need two weeks before each match so I can put them
    on.

They told me to play sweeper so I borrowed my mum's
    Hoover
and swept up their forward's shorts with a brilliant
    manoeuvre.
They asked about my shooting and how I could attack
so I got out my rifle but they made me put it back.

I told them that my dribbling was the best they'd get
then dribbled down their shirts and made them soaking
    wet.
They asked me to play winger, I said I couldn't fly.
'Well, mark your man instead' so I gave him two black
    eyes.

'Free kick!' said the ref, so I did and watched him fall.
Nobody had told me that I had to kick the ball.
In view of this the referee gave the other team the kick.
I was told to build a wall but I couldn't find a brick.

In the end there's only two positions I can play:
left back, right back in the changing rooms all day.
I'm only a beginner and someone could get hurt
so I don't have a number but an 'L' plate on my shirt.

At the Back of the Cupboard
under the Stairs

At the back of the cupboard under the stairs
deep in the shadows where nobody goes
something clicks, something whirs,
sometimes fast, sometimes slow,
sometimes high, sometimes low,
sometimes stop, sometimes go,
sometimes to, sometimes fro,
something stirs way down below.

At the back of the cupboard under the coats
deep in the shadows something creaks,
something tries to clear its throat,
something strong, something sleek,
something long, something bleak,
something freaky and unique,
something let out once a week,
something wants something to eat.

At the back of the cupboard under the stairs
deep in the shadows a creature roars,
something clicks, something whirs,
something just behind the door,
something waiting to explore,
something shaking on the floor,
something that you can't ignore,
something all of these and more.

A mouth that's wide and has no teeth
devouring everything beneath.
Flexible neck, adjustable throat,
dust-filled lungs that breathe out smoke.
A deathly monotone angry whine,
a long thin tail that gets entwined
tangling tables, strangling chairs,
roaming rooms, climbing stairs.

At the back of the cupboard under the stairs
deep in the shadows where nobody goes
something swallows dust and hairs,
nails from finger ends and toes,
sucked up scraps that decompose,
something lives, something grows,
something breathes, sucks and blows,
something waits to be exposed.

At the back of the cupboard under the stairs
. . . can you guess what it is hiding there?

A Superhero Sends a Letter Home

Dear Mum,

Things haven't been too good just lately.
Speeding bullets overtake me.
My dizzy spells and fear of heights
Inconvenience all my flights.
The purple tights you sent at last
Have given me a nasty rash.
X-ray vision's not all it seems
I'm sick of seeing bones and spleens.
My tinnitus is getting worse
The seams upon my trunks have burst.
I've got an aching in my head
I'm out of breath getting out of bed.
To top it all the yoghurt stains
On my satin cloak remain.
My love life hit a downward whirl
I'm no longer seeing Dandruff Girl.
She's gone off with Ali Tosis
The Bad Breath Boy who smells the
        mostest.
I'm scared of going out at night
I run away when I should fight.
So as you see things could be better
But not much worse as I end this letter.
My super powers are minus zero
Your loving son,

                        A failing hero
                        xxxx

Miss Smith's Mythical Bag

The curse of every class she'll see
No one knows its history
Its origin's a mystery
. . . Miss Smith's Mythical Bag.

Beyond our understanding
You dare not put your hand in
The bag that keeps expanding
. . . Miss Smith's Mythical Bag.

Broken chalk, a thousand pens with red ink that's
    congealed,
Forgotten fungus-covered bread with mouldy orange
    peel,
Lost car keys and headache pills, a Roman spear and
    shield,
Football cards and marbles, the goalposts from the field.

Where she goes it follows
All rippling lumps and hollows
The strangest things it swallows
. . . Miss Smith's Mythical Bag.

With a menacing unzipped grin it's
From the Outer Limits
There are black holes deep within it
. . . Miss Smith's Mythical Bag.

Crinkled tissues, Blu-tack balls, disfigured paperclips,
Sweets all covered up with fluff, dried up fibre-tips,
Lumps of powdered milk and coffee, last year's fish and
   chips,
From the Triangle in Bermuda – several missing ships.

Sometimes you hear it groan
Beyond the Twilight Zone
Make sure you're not alone
. . . with Miss Smith's Mythical Bag.

Shapeshifting, changing sizes,
The bag she never tidies,
It metamorphosizes
. . . Miss Smith's Mythical Bag.

More mysterious than Loch Ness, it's from the Fifth
   Dimension.
Stranger than an alien race beyond our comprehension.
Brooding with a strange intent that no one wants to
   mention
You'd better pay attention or you'll be in detention.

With Miss Smith's mythical, metaphysical,
astronomical, gastronomical, anatomical,
clinical, cynical bag!

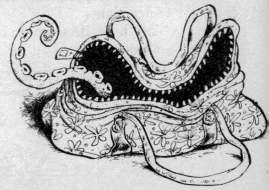

A Cautionary Verse (or Two)

Never play rugby with a dinner lady
Never try to juggle with a porcupine
Never have a bath with an alligator
Never taste and test food for a fly.

Never put piranhas on the toilet seat
Never burp in a silent test
Never sleep facedown on a bed of nails
Never go to school in your great gran's vest.

Never play cards with an octopus
Never play snap with a shark
Never keep ferrets in your underwear
Never make fun of a Doberman's bark.

Never make shoes for a millipede
Never milk a cow when it's a bull
Never try to find a rhyme for silver
Never talk to wolves when the moon is full.

Never take your clothes off in the staffroom
Never ignore your mummy's curse
Never play frisbee with Dad's records
Always listen to cautionary verse.

The Last Day of Summer

Shadows lengthen one last time
Ice cream vans hibernate
Shorts are banished to the bottom drawer
Cricket bats and tennis racquets revert to being pretend
   guitars
Barbecues burn sausages no more
Shirt sleeves roll down, not up
And somewhere under the stairs
There is the rustling of warmer coats
As woollen gloves gently wake from slumber
Deep inside their padded pocket nests.

Catch of the Day's Shoal
of the Season

Always choose an octopus for goalie.
Always have a whale for the defensive wall.
Always have a salmon for high crosses.
Never let a swordfish head the ball at all.

Never make an enemy of a sea anemone.
Never have a clash with a giant clam.
Never pull a mussel in a tackle or a tussle.
Always let the kipper be the skipper if you can.

Always have a mackerel to tackle well.
Always have a stingray staying on the wing.
Always have a shark – he's an expert at attack.
Never kiss a jellyfish who scores with a sting.

There are eels who feel electric playing at a pace that's
        hectic
and lobsters going potty scoring from an indirect kick.
There are dolphins doing dribbling weaving round
        shoals,
helping whelks, out-thinking winkles, getting lots of
        goals.

Mediterranean, Pacific and Atlantic,
the football is specific yet very very frantic.
Millions of matches of varying degrees
in the twenty thousand leagues under the seas.

The First Snow of Winter

Waking up to the scrunching carpet crunch,
the photographic negative,
the cotton-wool icing,
the transforming blanket
where even city centres could be Christmas cards
every child
delves in the understairs cupboard
for winter boots and wellies
wanting to be the first,
the very first, the very very first
to leave their mark, their print
and hear the sound of footprints in the snow.

Sayings for People Who Can't Spell

Don't put all your legs in one basket
Don't be a sight for four eyes
Don't count your chickens before they're thatched
Don't watch too much telly, you'll get square thighs

Don't speak with your mouth foul
Don't give a dog new ticks
Don't cheat with your mouth open
Don't get the long end of the sick

Don't cry over spit milk
Don't fall head over wheels
Don't be as sick as a carrot
Don't be as lippy as an eel

Don't be as stubborn as a mole
Don't be a bear with a sore shed
Don't stick out like a sore bum
Don't put ideas in someone's bed

Don't have crocodile ears
If you can't stand the feet get out of the kitchen
Don't get your knickers in a twit
And be careful - Ruth is stranger than fiction.

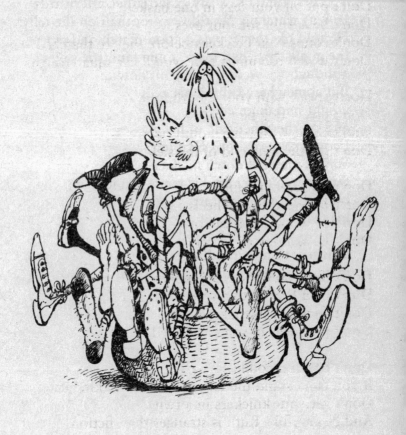

Losing at Home

I never really cried when my grandma died.
You see I was away from home at the time.
The first time I saw my grandfather afterwards
he was watching World Cup football on the telly.
He told me that it was a good match and that
the goalkeeper had made some fantastic saves
although we were still one nil down.
But somewhere behind his eyes
a light had dimmed
and on the other side of his glasses
I could see teardrops forming
and as they fell down his face
they weren't because his team had lost
but because he had lost
his team.

You see, to my grandfather
my grandmother was his best team
in the world.
Ever.

Wizard with the Ball

Young Arthur Merlin's spellbinding
His skills are crystal clear
A wizard with the ball
He makes it disappear!

Which is very useful in the opposition's penalty area.

Coolscorin' Matchwinnin'
Celebratin' Striker!

I'm a shirt removin' crowd salutin'
handstandin' happy landin'
rockin' rollin' divin' slidin'
posin' poutin' loud shoutin'
pistol packin' smoke blowin'
flag wavin' kiss throwin'
hipswinging' armwavin'
breakdancin' cool ravin'
shoulder shruggin' team huggin'
hot shootin' rootin' tootin'
somersaultin' fence vaultin'
last-minute goal grinnin'
shimmy shootin' shin spinnin'
celebratin' cup winnin' STRIKER!

It's Not the Same Any More

It's not the same since Patch died.
Sticks are just sticks.
Never thrown, never fetched.

It's not the same any more.
Tennis balls lie still and lifeless.
The urge to bounce them has gone.

It's not the same now.
I can't bring myself to whistle.
There's no reason to do so.

His collar hangs on the hook
and his name tag and lead are dusty.

His basket and bowl are in a plastic bag
lying at an angle on a garage shelf.

My new slippers will never be chewed
and I've no excuse for my lack of homework any more.

I can now watch the football in peace, uninterrupted.
No frantic barking and leaping just when it gets to the
    goal.

I don't have to share my sweets and biscuits
and then wipe the dribbling drool off my trouser legs.

It's just not the same any more.
When Patch died a small part of me died too.

All that's left is a mound of earth
and my hand-made cross beneath the apple tree.

All that's left are the memories.
Thousands of them.

It's just not the same any more.

I Wish I'd Been Present at Christmas Past

I wish I'd been a shepherd
and heard the angels sing.
I wish I'd been to Bethlehem
and seen the Infant King.

I wish I'd been a wise man
at the stable bare
following the star with
gold, frankincense and myrrh.

I wish I'd been an animal
who shared my manger hay
with that special newborn baby
on that first Christmas Day.

Stairway to the Clouds

I took a stairway to the clouds
And a camel to the moon
A trampoline to Timbuktu
And a rocket to my room

A skateboard to the Red Sea
A submarine to Mars
A freight train to Atlantis
I dived up to the stars

Parachuting on the ocean
I rode my bike down deep
I took a racing car to bed
And drove myself to sleep

I caught a bus that flew
To a bridge across the seas
And then in my canoe
I slalomed through the trees

I scootered on thin ice
Space-hoppered into space
With ice skates on the running track
I raced the human race

I bounced upon my pogo stick
All round the equator
I scaled the peak of Everest
Thanks to an elevator

I rope swung in the city
Piggy-backed through town
Rode horses down the rivers
Skied deep down underground

I swim across the deserts
And surf on escalators
I rollerskate on glaciers
And leapfrog high skyscrapers

I've travelled many places
In my different styles
Near and far and deep and wide
Millions of miles.

But no matter how I wander
No matter where I roam
Of all these special journeys
The best one is . . . back home.

Sea Shoals See Shows on the Sea Bed

The salmon with a hat on was conducting with a baton
and it tried to tune the tuna fish by playing on its scales
the scales had all been flattened when the tuna fish was
    sat on
on purpose by a porpoise and a school of killer whales.
So the salmon with a hat on fiddled with his baton
while the angelfish got ready to play the tambourine.
Things began to happen when the salmon with a baton
was tapping out a pattern for the band of the marines.

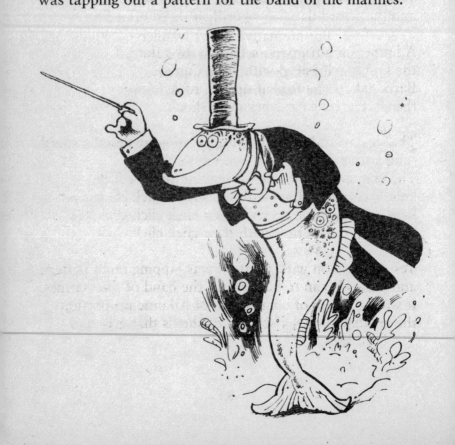

There was a minnow on piano, a prawn with a horn,
an otter on guitar looking all forlorn.
A whale-voice choir and a carp with a harp,
a belly-dancing jellyfish jiving with a shark.

The octaves on the octopus played the middle eight
but they couldn't keep in tune with the skiffle-playing
    skate.
The plaice on the bass began to rock and roll
with the bloater on a boater and a Dover sole.

A clam on castanets, an eel on glockenspiel,
an oyster in a cloister singing with a seal.
The haddock had a headache from the deafening din
and the sword-dancing swordfish sliced off a fin.

A limpet on a trumpet, a flatfish on a flute,
the kipper fell asleep with King Canute.
Barracuda on a tuba sat upon a rock,
the electric eel gave everyone a shock.

The shrimp and the sturgeon, the stingray and the squid
sang a four-part harmony on the sea bed.
The crab and the lobster gave their claws a flick,
kept everyone in time with their click click click . . .
kept everyone in time with their click click click . . .
kept everyone in time with their click click click . . .

Yes, the salmon with a hat on was tapping out a pattern
and things began to happen for the band of the marines.
It was an ocean of commotion of Atlantic proportion
the greatest show by schools of shoals that ever had
    been seen.

The Haunted Poem

This poem is haunted by a ghost.
No one has ever seen him
but every single person who reads this poem
will be left in no doubt of his existence.

Sometimes he changes the order of words the,
mixes the lettwfasahj4el8r7fn666s pu
or even makes them   .

You'll be halfway through the **BOO!**
verse and he'll interrupt and make you jump.

While sections are w^{O}o^{O}o^{O}o^{O}o filled
with his WOO HOO spooky moaning and groaning
then suddenly fade away.

At any time he may frighten you
or add rude words when you're not bum expecting it
so that when knickerscheesytoes you read them
you blush and go bright GOTCHA! red.

HAHAHAHAAA!
his laughter will echo in your brain
HAHAHAHAAA!
and ring constantly ring constantly ring ring constantly
HAHAHAHAAA!
in your ears
HAHAHAHAAA!

Even now he is watching your every move
as you read the haunted poem . . .
every twitch, every blink, every sigh, every glance,
so that just when you think you've read the last word
and the poem is over he leaves a ghostly message,
just for you . . .

Watch out behind you

An Ordinary Week

Sunday:
Went to visit Granny as usual. Bor-ring. She lives miles
away. Took ages to get there. She lives somewhere called
Mount Veryest. It's really high and she has a Yet Petty.
Mum made me wear a vest and mittens with elastic on.

Monday:
Ho hum – school again. Had to write a story called
'Exciting things I did at the weekend'. Couldn't think of
anything.

Tuesday:
Got a merit mark for my science homework with my
methane-powered space rocket built from dustbins, a
bike frame, the baby's pram, Grandad's wellies and the
chicken muck from the shed. Blast off went well – blew
the headmaster's wig off.

Wednesday:
Mum had to help with my music homework. Finished
off a symphony by someone called Batehoover.
Particularly pleased with the banjo solo.

Thursday:
Had to stay off school. Brother put superglue on the
toilet seat. Dad was stuck on there all day. Nothing new.
I had to call the ambulance.

Friday:
Discovered dinosaur bones underneath garden shed.

Saturday:
Played football. Really big pitch. Loads of people
watched. Called Womberley I think. We won. Got a cup
and medal. And met the Queen. Late home. Got told
off.

Index of First Lines

The very best poetry available from Macmillan

The prices shown below are correct at the time of going to press. However, Macmillan Publishers reserve the right to show new retail prices on covers which may differ from those previously advertised.

The Very Best of Richard Edwards	0 330 39389 8	£3.99
The Very Best of Ian McMillan	0 330 39365 0	£3.99
The Very Best of Vernon Scannell	0 330 48344 7	£3.99
The Very Best of Paul Cookson	0 330 48014 6	£3.99
The Very Best of David Harmer	0 330 48190 8	£3.99
The Very Best of Wes Magee	0 330 48192 4	£3.99

All Macmillan titles can be ordered at your local bookshop or are available by post from:

Book Service by Post
PO Box 29, Douglas, Isle of Man IM99 1BQ

Credit cards accepted. For details:
Telephone: 01624 675137
Fax: 01624 670923
E-mail: bookshop@enterprise.net

Free postage and packing in the UK.
Overseas customers: add £1 per book (paperback)
and £3 per book (hardback).